The High IQ Society

BRAIN
FIT

THIS IS A CARLTON BOOK

This edition published in 2010 by
Carlton Books Limited
20 Mortimer Street
London W1T 3JW

ISBN: 978-1-84732-723-9

Printed in China

The puzzles in this book previously appeared in
Mensa Puzzle Challenge and *Mensa Puzzle Challenge 2*

Mensa
The High IQ Society

BRAIN
FIT

**Exercise your brain with these
challenging puzzles**

CARLTON
BOOKS

Mensa is the international society for people with a high IQ.
We have more than 100,000 members in over 40 countries
worldwide.

The society's aims are:
> to identify and foster human intelligence for the benefit of
> humanity
> to encourage research in the nature, characteristics, and uses
> of intelligence
> to provide a stimulating intellectual and social environment
> for its members

Anyone with an IQ score in the top two per cent of population is
eligible to become a member of Mensa – are you the 'one in 50' we've
been looking for?

Mensa membership offers an excellent range of benefits:
> Networking and social activities nationally and around the world
> Special Interest Groups – hundreds of chances to pursue your
> hobbies and interests – from art to zoology!
> Monthly members' magazine and regional newsletters
> Local meetings – from games challenges to food and drink
> National and international weekend gatherings and conferences
> Intellectually stimulating lectures and seminars
> Access to the worldwide SIGHT network for travellers and hosts

For more information about Mensa: www.mensa.org, or

British Mensa Ltd.,
St John's House,
St John's Square,
Wolverhampton
WV2 4AH
Telephone: +44 (0) 1902 772771
E-mail: enquiries@mensa.org.uk
www.mensa.org.uk

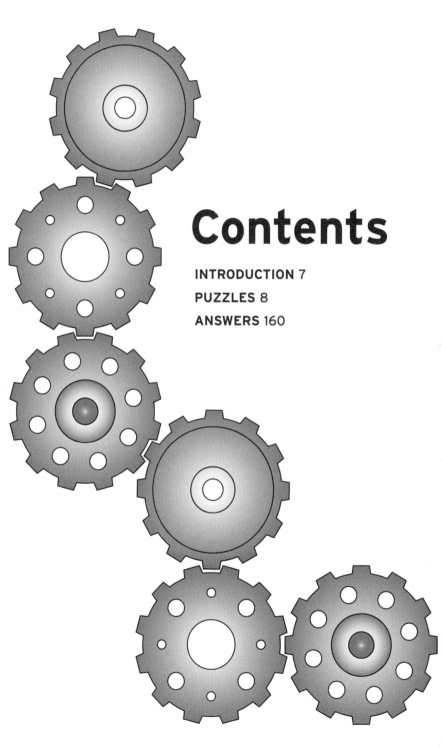

Contents

Introduction

Welcome to the pages of this colourful brain fitness book. We hope you will find it stimulating and helpful, that it keeps you busy and becomes part of your daily brain fit workout. There are more than 130 puzzles for you here, some fairly easy and some really tough. Which ones are which is up to you, to a certain extent – different people find differing puzzle types easy or tough, depending on their personalities and solving methods. But if you get stuck while solving, just take a few moments to stop and think about something else – maybe even another puzzle, before you come back and have another go. Sometimes this will be all you need to either figure out the answer or get the necessary flash of inspiration. And don't worry if you get really really stuck – we've included the answers at the end as a last resort!

So have fun, work hard and enjoy keeping your brain fit!

The puzzles

Can you work out which two sides on these cubes contain the same symbols?

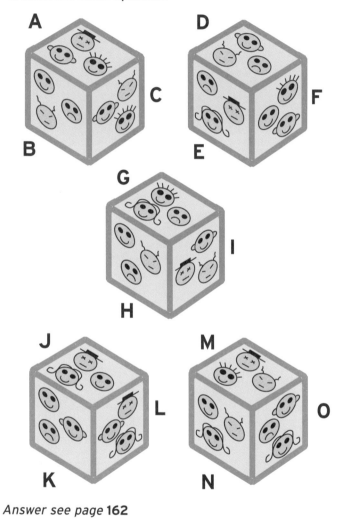

Answer see page **162**

Can you work out which is the odd ball out?

Answer see page **162**

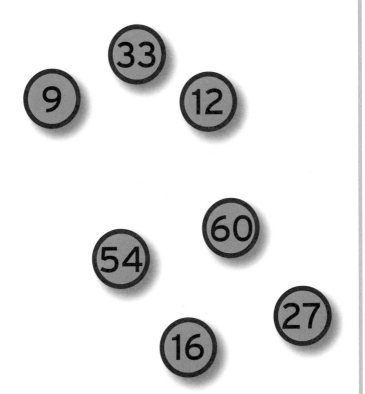

Can you replace the question marks with + or – so that both sections in this diagram add up to the same value?

Answer see page **162**

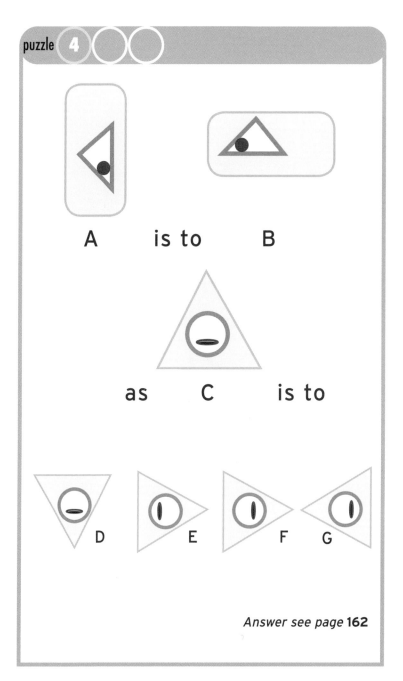

A   is to   B

as   C   is to

D   E   F   G

Answer see page 162

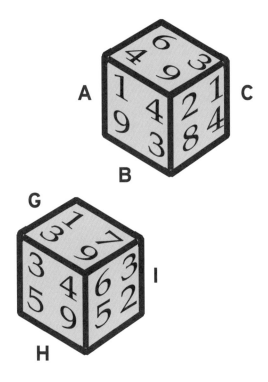

Two sides of these cubes contain exactly the same numbers. Can you spot them?

Answer see page **162**

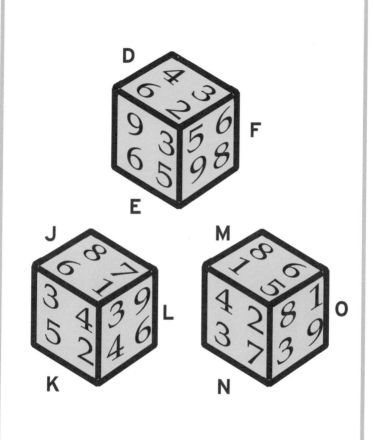

Can you find the mathematical signs that should replace the question marks in this diagram?

Answer see page **162**

The four triangles are linked by a simple mathematical formula. Can you discover what it is and then find the odd one out?

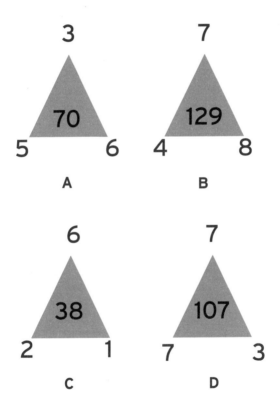

3

70

5   6

A

7

129

4   8

B

6

38

2   1

C

7

107

7   3

D

Answer see page 162

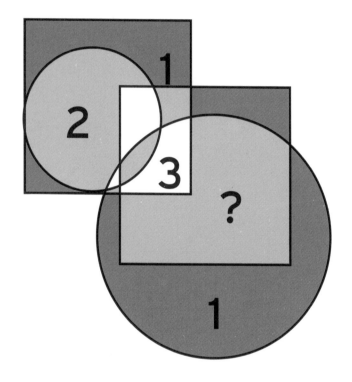

Can you crack the logic of this diagram and replace the question mark with a number?

Answer see page **162**

How would you continue this series?

12345

Answer see page **162**

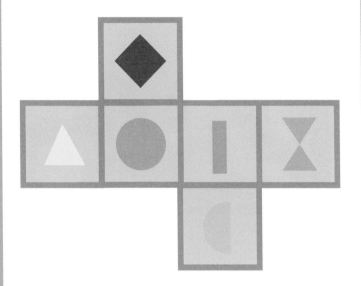

Which of these cubes cannot be made from this layout?

Answer see page 162

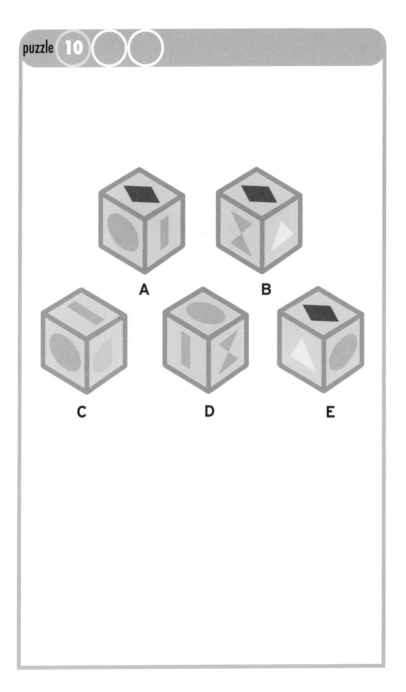

A B

C D E

Can you replace the question marks in this diagram with the symbols x and ÷ so that both sections arrive at the same value?

Answer see page 162

Can you work out which three sides of these cubes contain the same symbols?

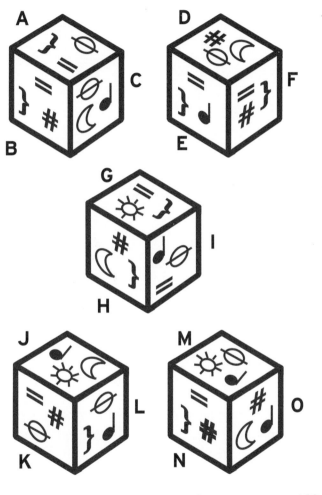

Answer see page **162**

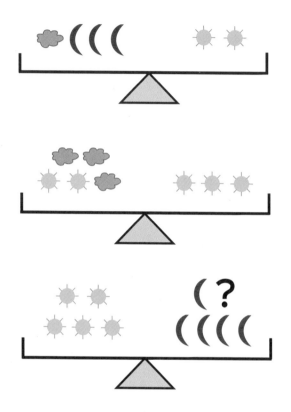

Each of the symbols represents a value. Which symbols would you need to add to balance the last scale?

Answer see page 162

Can you work out which of these balls is the odd one out?

Answer see page **162**

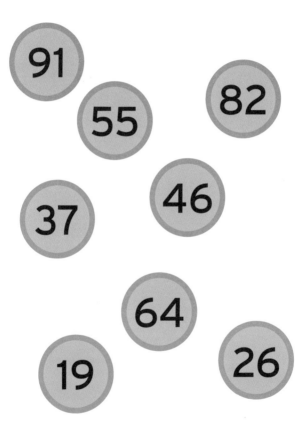

These tiles when placed in the right order will form a square in which the first horizontal line is identical with the first vertical line, and so. Can you successfully form the square?

Answer see page **162**

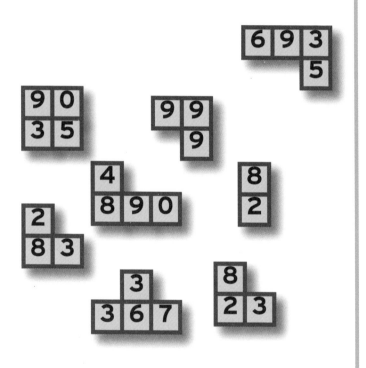

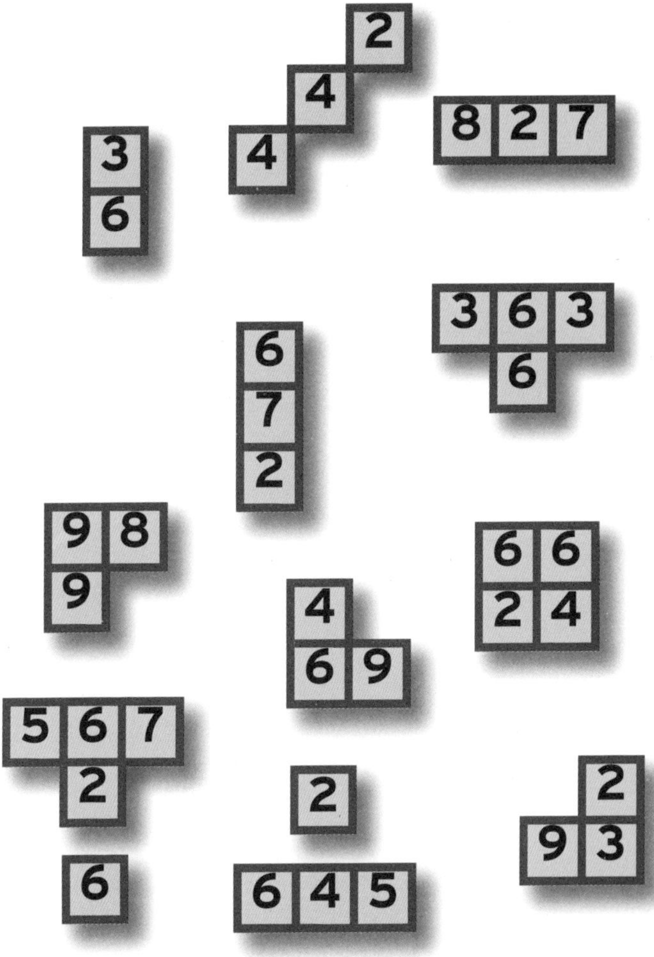

2
4
4

8 2 7

3
6

3 6 3
6

6
7
2

9 8
9

6 6
2 4

5 6 7
2

4
6 9

6

2

2
9 3

6 4 5

Can you work out what number should replace the question mark in the square?

Answer see page **163**

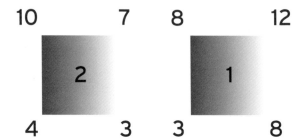

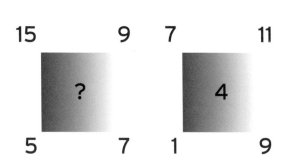

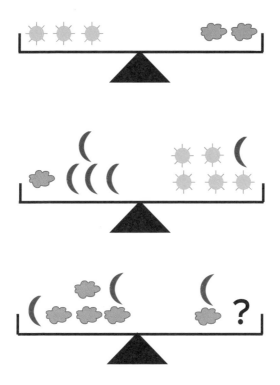

Can you work out which symbols should replace the question mark, so that the scales balance?

Answer see page **163**

Can you find the odd one out of these symbols?

Answer see page **163**

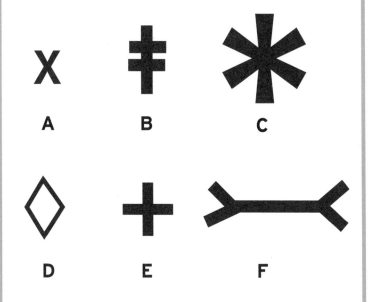

Can you work out what number should replace the question mark to follow the rules of the other wheels?

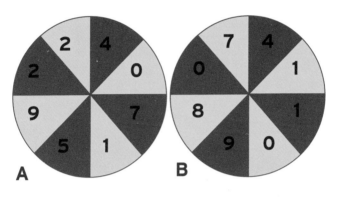

A

B

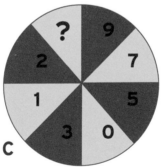

C

Answer see page 163

In this diagram, starting from the top of the diamond and working in a clockwise direction, the four basic mathematical signs (+, −, x, ÷) have been omitted. Your task is to restore them so that the calculation, with the answer in the middle, is correct.

Answer see page **163**

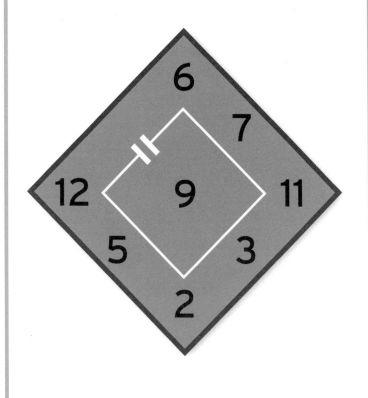

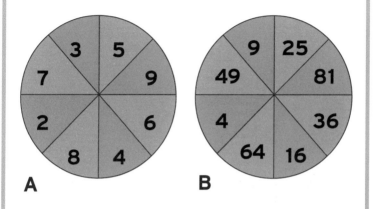

A

B

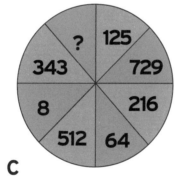

C

A curious logic governs the numbers in these circles. Can you discover what it is and then work out what the missing number should be?

Answer see page 163

puzzle 22

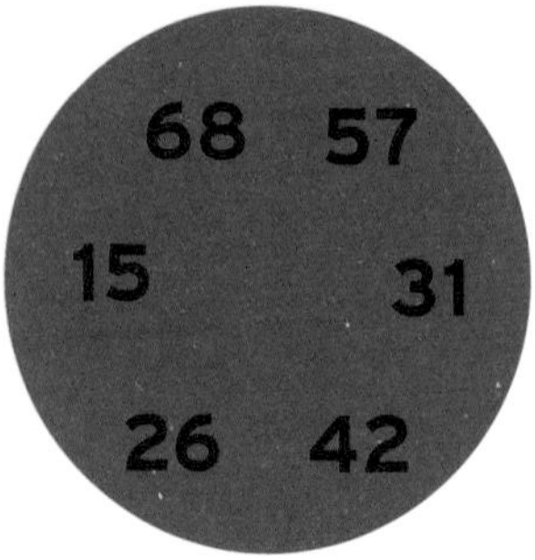
68 57
15 31
26 42

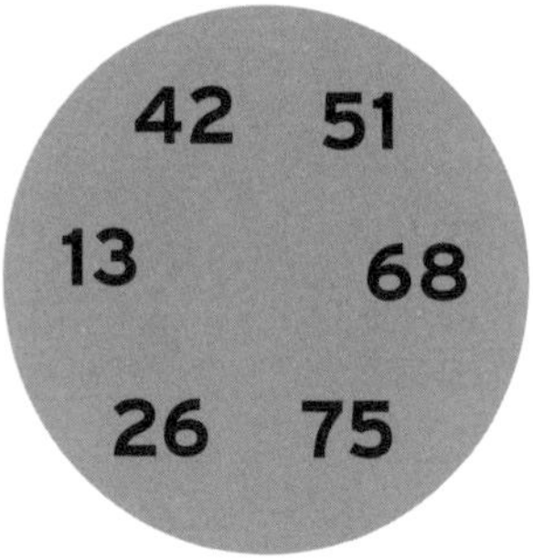
42 51
13 68
26 75

A is to B

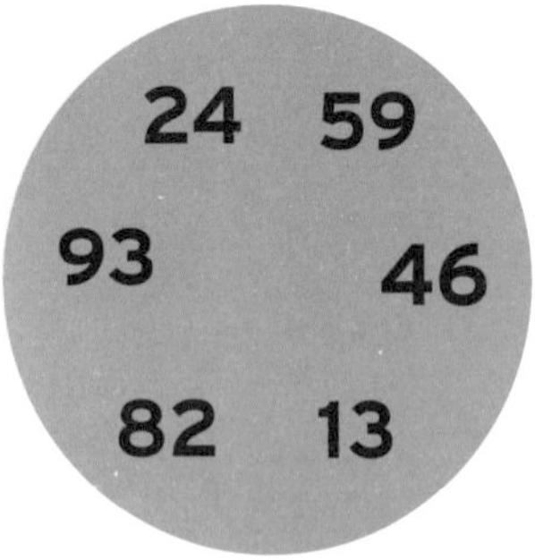
24 59
93 46
82 13

as C is to

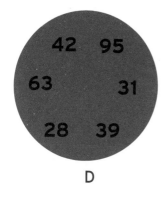

D

E

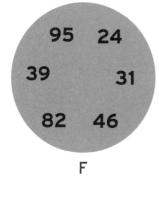

F

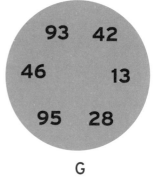

G

Answer see page 163

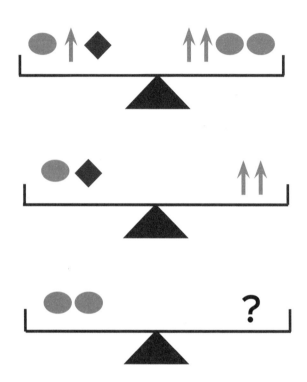

Can you find out which symbol would balance the third scale?

Answer see page **163**

Can you work out which of these diagrams is
different from the others?

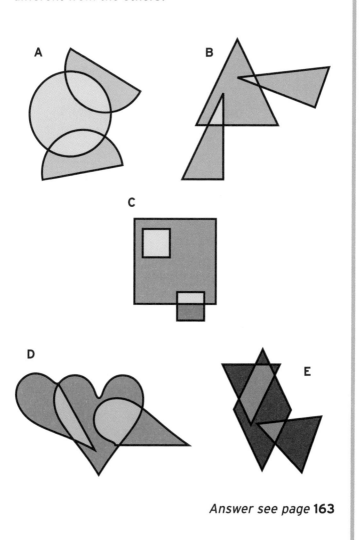

A

B

C

D

E

Answer see page **163**

Can you work out what the blank clockface should look like?

Answer see page **164**

1

2

3

4

35   47   38   24

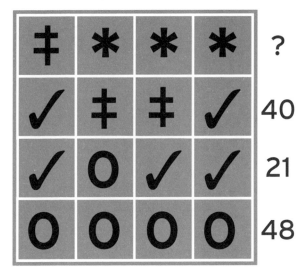

Can you work out what number each symbol
represents and find the value of the question mark?

Answer see page 164

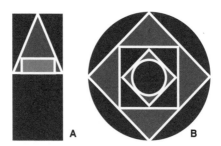

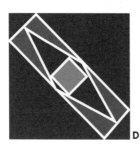

Which is the odd one out?

Answer see page **164**

Look at the clock faces shown below. Choose one
from the second row to continue the series.

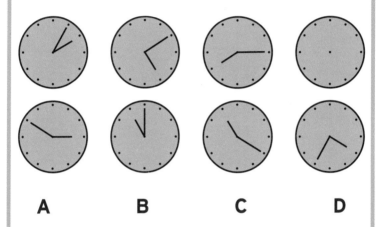

A   B   C   D

Answer see page 164

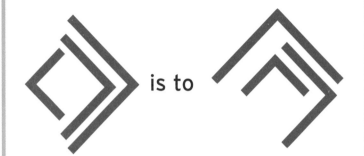 is to

as  is to:

Answer see page **164**

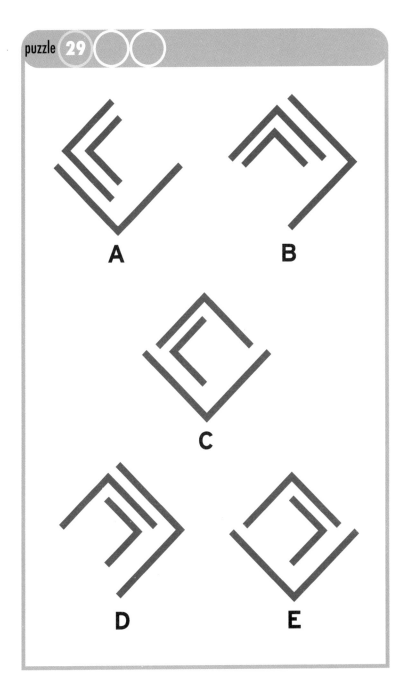

A

B

C

D

E

Which of these shapes forms a perfect triangle when combined with the picture below?

Answer see page **164**

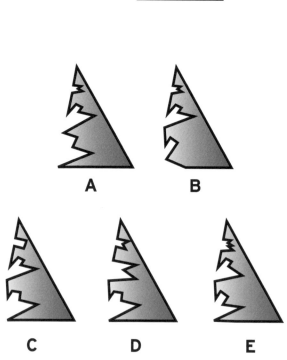

A   **B**

C   **D**   **E**

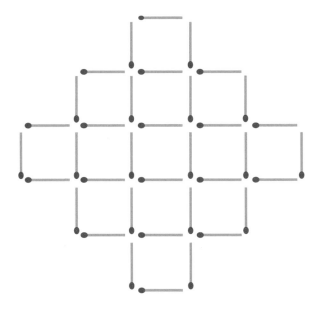

By taking away four matches from this diagram, leave eight small squares.

Answer see page 164

Which is the odd one out?

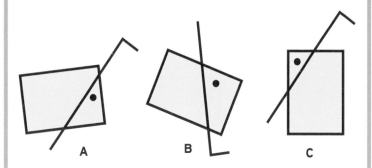

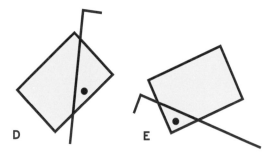

Answer see page **164**

Which is the odd one out?

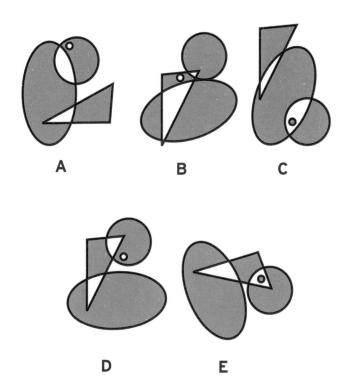

A   B   C

D   E

Answer see page **164**

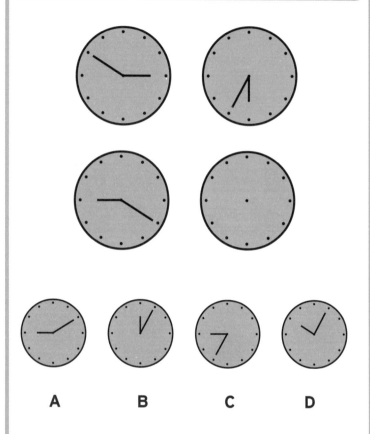

A   **B**   **C**   **D**

Another series of clock faces. Again it is up to you to work out the logic behind the series of and pick the clock from the bottom row that replaces the blank clock.

Answer see page **164**

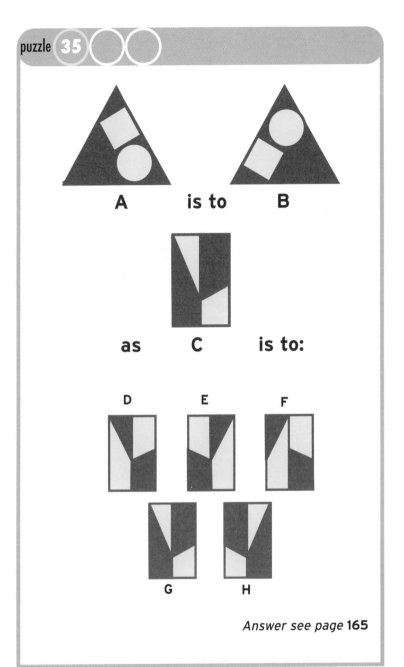

A   is to   B

as   C   is to:

D   E   F

G   H

Answer see page **165**

Which image comes next in the sequence?

Answer see page **165**

A

B

C

D

E

Can you work out which sides on these cubes contain the same letters?

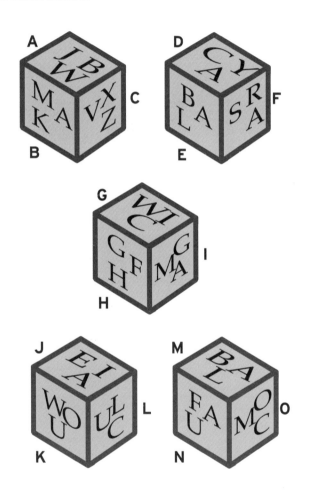

Answer see page 165

What letter replaces the question mark in this star?

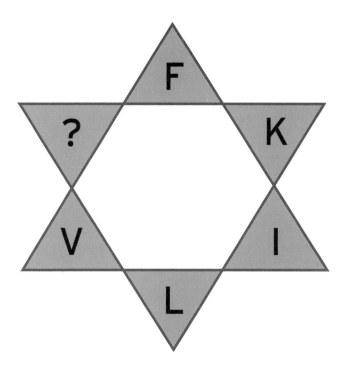

Answer see page 165

In this diamond the mathematical signs +, -, x and ÷ have been left out. Can you work out which sign fits between each pair of numbers to arrive at the number in the middle of the diagram? To start you off, three of the signs are each used twice.

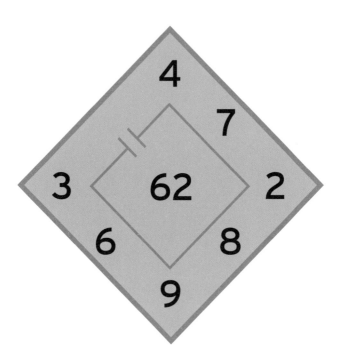

Answer see page **165**

Can you work out the number needed to complete the square?

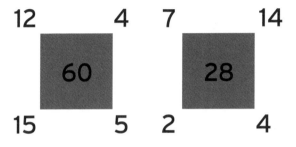

12 4   7   14
   60   28
15 5   2   4

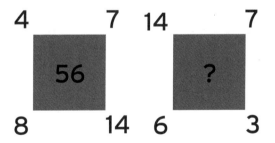

4   7   14   7
  56   ?
8   14   6   3

Answer see page 165

Someone has made a mistake decorating this cake.
Can you correct the pattern?

Answer see page **165**

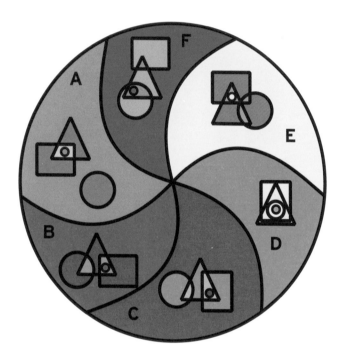

Find a number that could replace the question mark.
Each colour represents a number under 10.

Answer see page 165

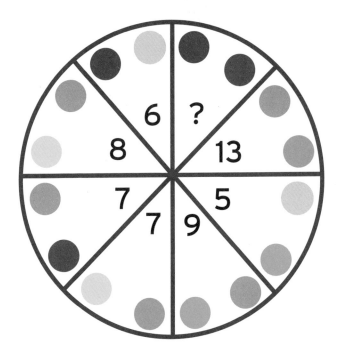

Can you spot the cube that cannot be
made from the layout below?

Answer see page **165**

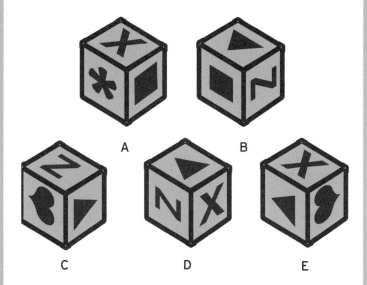

A

B

C

D

E

Can you work out the reasoning behind these squares and replace the question mark with a number?

12   19   17   6

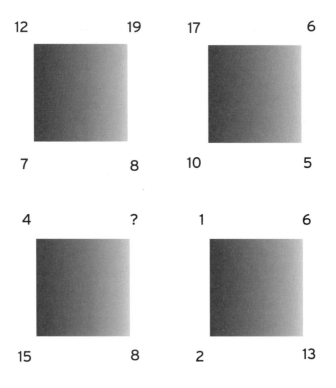

7   8   10   5

4   ?   1   6

15   8   2   13

Answer see page 165

Can you find the number that should replace the question mark?

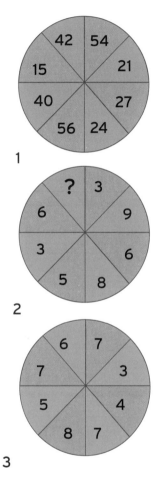

1

2

3

Answer see page **165**

Can you work out the reasoning behind this square and replace the question mark with the correct shape?

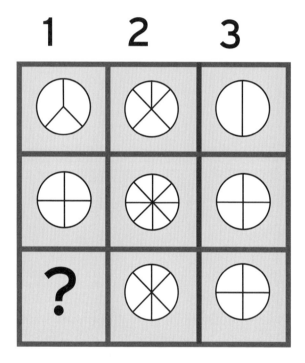

Answer see page 166

Five cyclists are taking part in a race. The number of each rider and his cycling time are related to each other. Can you work out the number of the last cyclist?

No. 9

Takes 1 hr 35

No. 10

Takes 1 hr 43

No. 11

Takes 1 hr 52

No. 14

Takes 2 hr 27

No. ?

Takes 2 hr 33

Answer see page 166

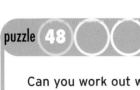

Can you work out which diagram would continue the series?

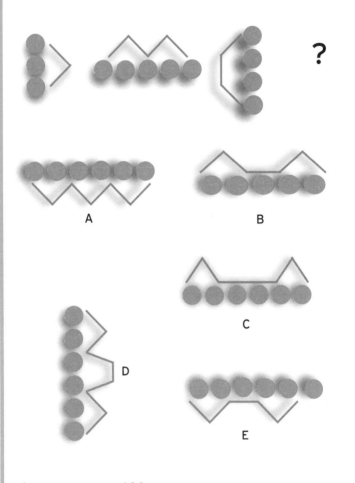

A

B

C

D

E

Answer see page **166**

Find the missing number.

6   3

11
4   2

4   8
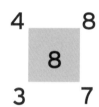
8
3   7

5   3
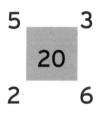
20
2   6

6   2
?
1   4

Answer see page 166

Which of these cubes can be made from the above layout?

Answer see page **166**

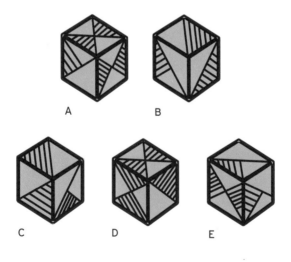

A

B

C

D

E

Can you work out which of these symbols follows the sequence?

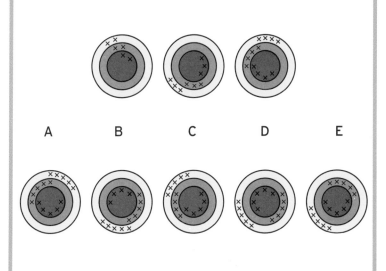

A   B   C   D   E

Answer see page **166**

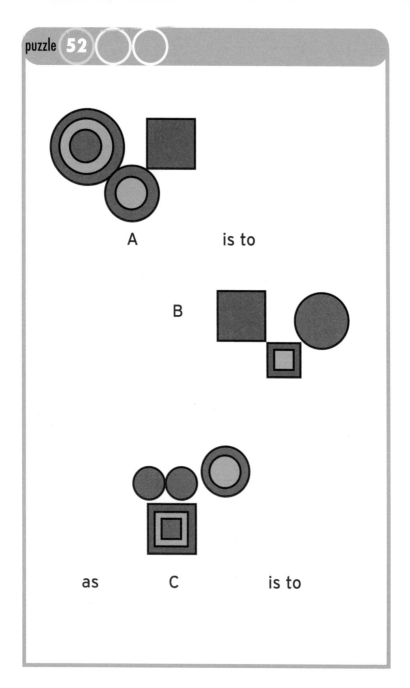

A   is to

B

as   C   is to

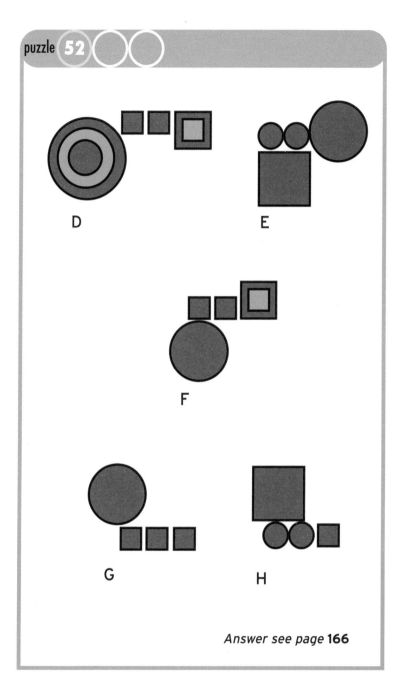

D

E

F

G

H

Answer see page **166**

Can you work out what the next grid in the sequence below should look like?

?

Answer see page **167**

Can you work out which of these cubes cannot be made from the this layout?

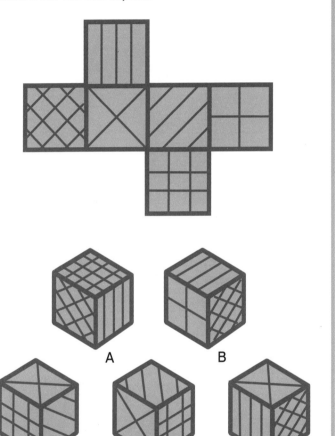

A

B

C

D

E

Answer see page 167

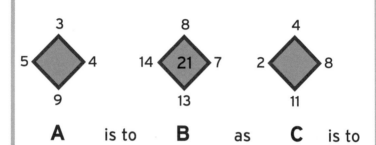

3
5 4
9

A   is to

8
14 **21** 7
13

B   as

4
2 8
11

C   is to

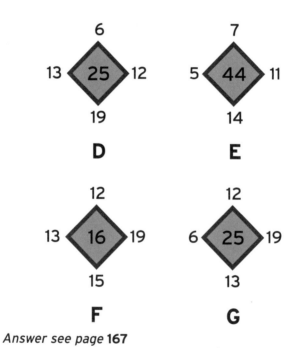

6
13 **25** 12
19

D

7
5 **44** 11
14

E

12
13 **16** 19
15

F

12
6 **25** 19
13

G

Answer see page **167**

Each horse carries a weight handicap.

Can you work out the number of the final horse?

No. 4 15kg

No. 7 18kg

No. 3 14kg

No. 8 19kg

No. ? 24kg

Answer see page **167**

Can you find the shape that would continue the series above?

A   B   C

D   E

Answer see page **167**

Can you work out the reasoning behind these squares and find the missing number?

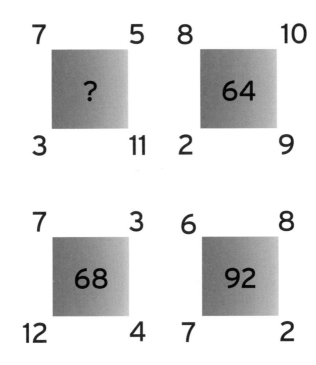

7	5	8	10
?		64	
3	11	2	9

7	3	6	8
68		92	
12	4	7	2

Answer see page 167

All these bikes took part in an overnight race. Something really weird happened! The start and finish times of the bikes became mathematically linked. If you can discover the link you should be able to decide when bike D finished.

Answer see page 167

A START 3:15

FINISH 2:06

B START 3:20

FINISH 1:09

C START 5:24

FINISH 2:11

D START 7:35

FINISH ?

E START 6:28

FINISH 4:22

To which of these diagrams could you add a circle
to match the conditions of the figure at the top?

Answer see page **168**

Which of the sections shown would logically complete the puzzle?

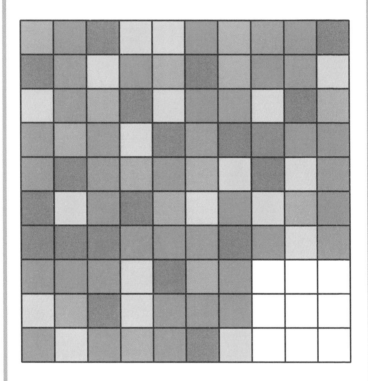

A

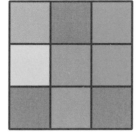

B

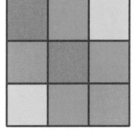

C

Answer see page **168**

Which of these shapes fits to complete the polygon?

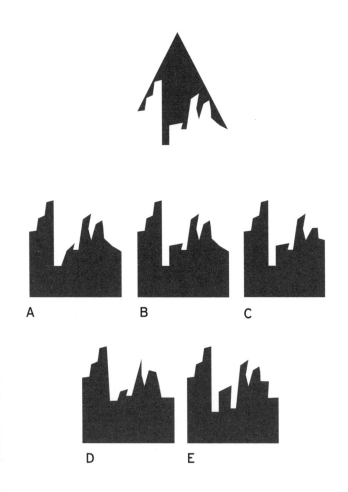

A

B

C

D

E

Answer see page **168**

Can you replace the question mark with a number?

Answer see page **168**

4	x	**3**	**+**	**8**
=			**÷**
5			**2**
-			**+**
?	x	**7**	**÷**	**11**

Can you work out which of these squares is the odd one out?

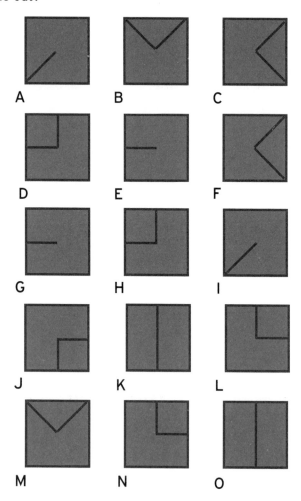

A

B

C

D

E

F

G

H

I

J

K

L

M

N

O

Answer see page **168**

Can you find the odd shape out?

Answer see page **168**

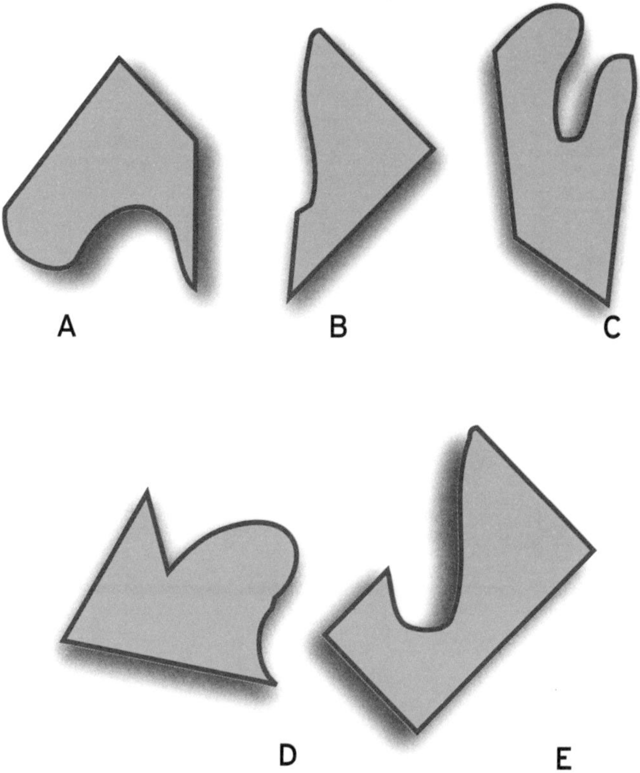

A

B

C

D

E

Can you work out what number should replace
the question mark?

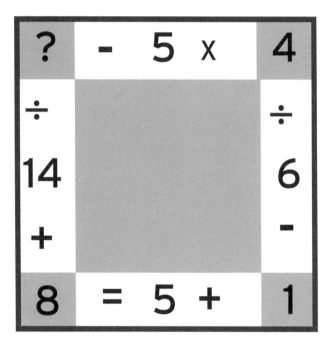

Answer see page **168**

Can you work out what number should replace the question mark?

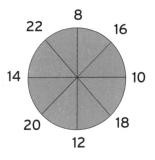

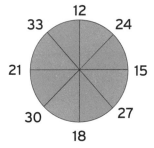

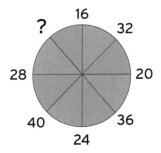

Answer see page **168**

Which cube can be made from this layout?

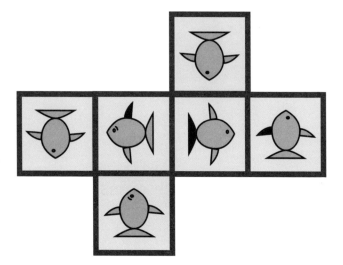

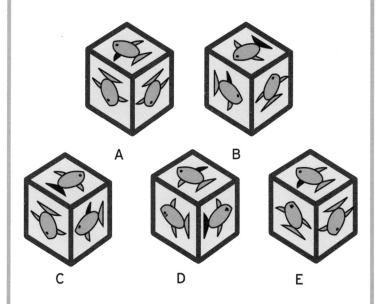

A

B

C

D

E

Answer see page 168

Can you find the odd shape out?

Answer see page **168**

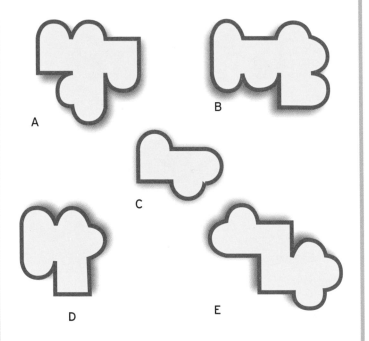

Can you work out what the missing section in the last wheel should look like?

Answer see page **169**

Can you work out what the next wheel in this sequence should look like?

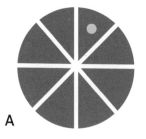

A

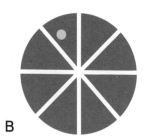

B

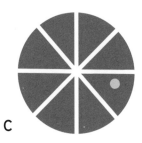

C

D

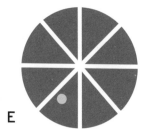

E

Answer see page **169**

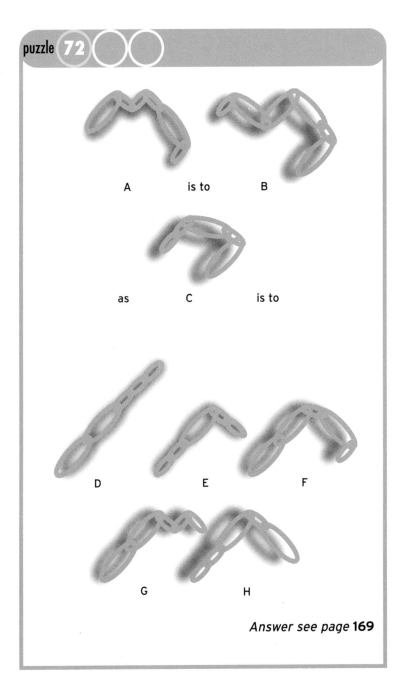

A   is to   B

as   C   is to

D   E   F

G   H

Answer see page **169**

Can you work out the reasoning behind these squares and find the number that should replace the question mark?

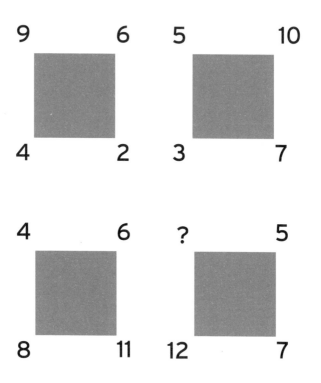

9   6   5   10

4   2   3   7

4   6   ?   5

8   11   12   7

Answer see page 169

Can you find the odd shape out?

A

B

C

D

E

Answer see page **169**

Can you find the odd diagram out?

Answer see page **169**

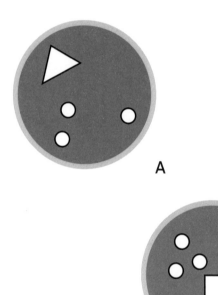

A

B

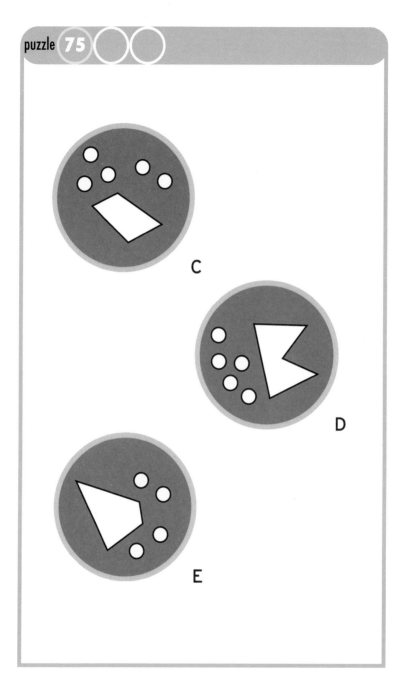

C

D

E

Can you work out the logic behind these triangles and replace the question mark with a number?

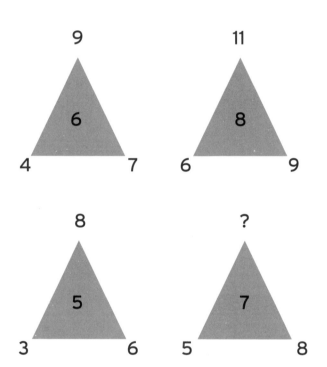

Answer see page **169**

Can you work out what number should replace the question mark?

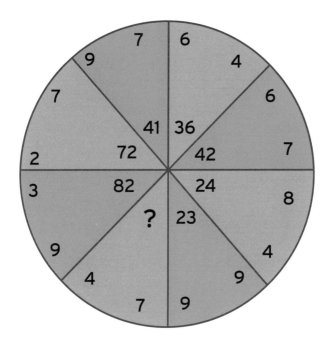

Answer see page **169**

Five cyclists are taking part in a race. The number of each rider and its arrival time are in some way related. Can you work out the number of the rider who arrives at 2:30?

No. 10

Arrives 2:15

No. 2

Arrives 3:02

No. 30

Arrives 2:45

No. 8

Arrives 3:08

No. ?

Arrives 2:30

Answer see page 170

Using the amounts of time specified, can you work out whether you have to go forward or backward to get from the time on the top clock to that on the bottom clock?

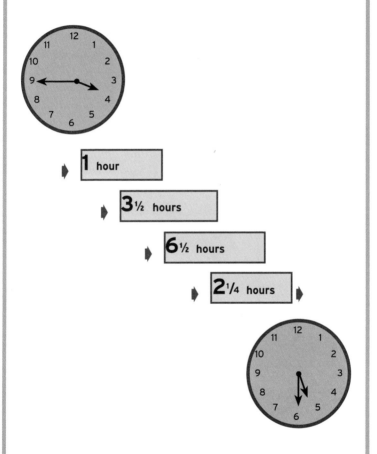

1 hour

3½ hours

6½ hours

2¼ hours

Answer see page **170**

Can you work out the reasoning behind this square and replace the question mark with a number?

Answer see page **170**

5	3	8	7
12	15	49	56
3	9	4	12
18	27	36	?

Which of these shapes should replace the question mark?

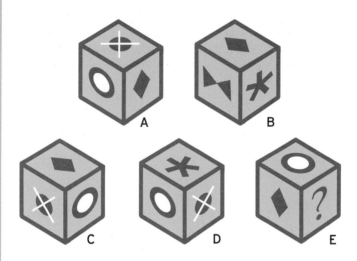

A

B

C

D

E

Answer see page 170

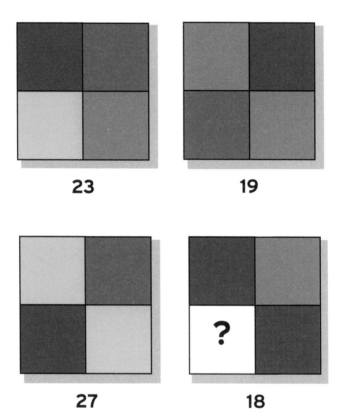

What colour replaces the question mark?

23

19

27

18

Answer see page **170**

Can you work out which of these symbols follows the sequence above?

Answer see page **170**

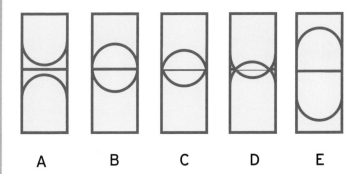

A   B   C   D   E

Can you work out the reasoning behind these triangles and replace the question mark with a number?

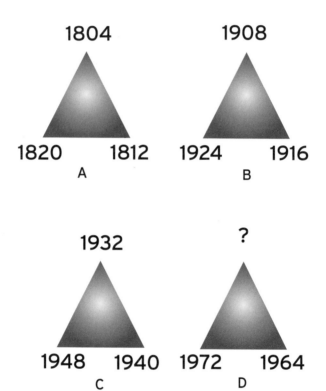

1804

1820   1812
A

1908

1924   1916
B

1932

1948   1940
C

?

1972   1964
D

Answer see page 170

The following clock faces are in some way related. Can you work out what the time on clock No. 3 should be?

1

2

3

4

Answer see page 170

Can you work out what number should replace the question mark in this square?

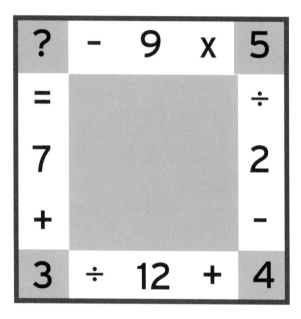

?	–	9	x	5
=				÷
7				2
+				–
3	÷	12	+	4

Answer see page **170**

Which diagram is the odd one out?

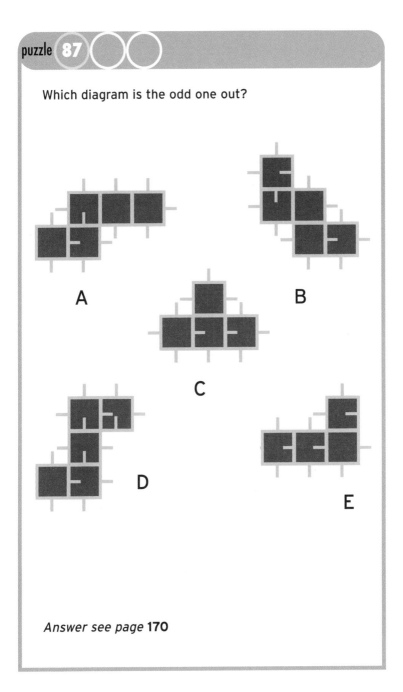

A

B

C

D

E

Answer see page **170**

Can you work out which of these cubes is not the same as the others?

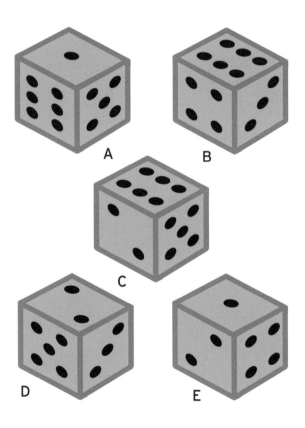

A

B

C

D

E

Answer see page **170**

Each tractor gathers potatoes over a certain acreage (shown in brackets). The weight of potatoes in kilos is shown under each tractor. There is a relationship between the number of the tractor, the acreage and the weight gathered. What weight should tractor B show?

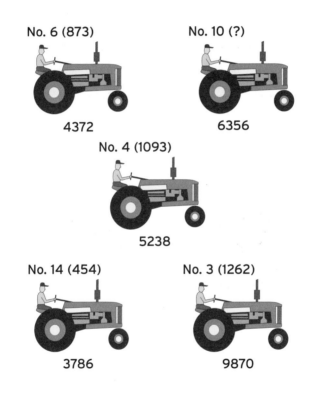

No. 6 (873)

4372

No. 10 (?)

6356

No. 4 (1093)

5238

No. 14 (454)

3786

No. 3 (1262)

9870

Answer see page **171**

Can you unravel the logic behind these squares and find the missing number?

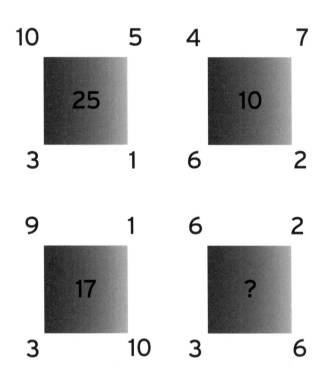

10		5		4		7
	25				**10**	
3		1		6		2

9		1		6		2
	17				**?**	
3		10		3		6

Answer see page **171**

Can you find the missing number in this square?

1536	48	96	3
384	192	24	12
768	96	48	6
192	?	12	24

Answer see page 171

Can you work out what the next flower in this series should look like?

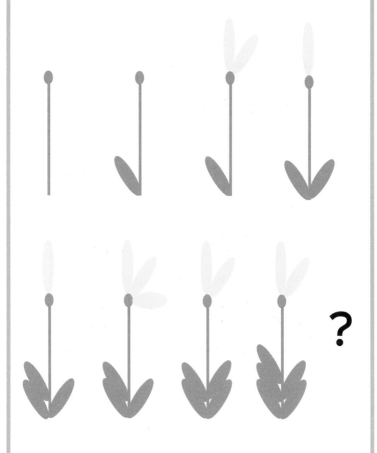

Answer see page 171

32   41   ?

Can you find the number that fits below the 7?

Answer see page **171**

Can you unravel the reasoning behind this wheel and replace the question mark with a number?

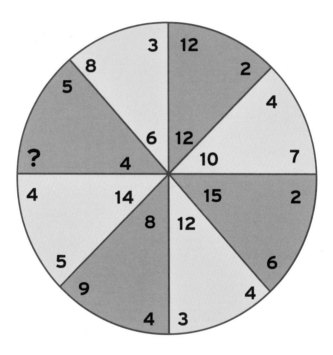

Answer see page **171**

Can you unravel the logic behind this diagram and find the missing number?

Answer see page **172**

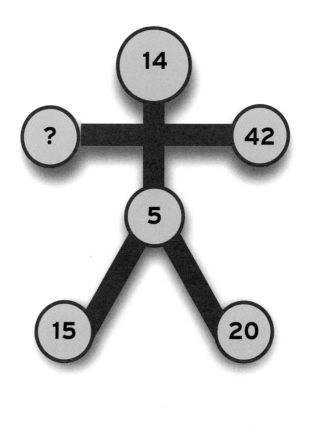

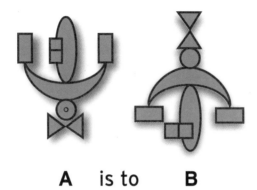

A is to **B**

as **C** is to:

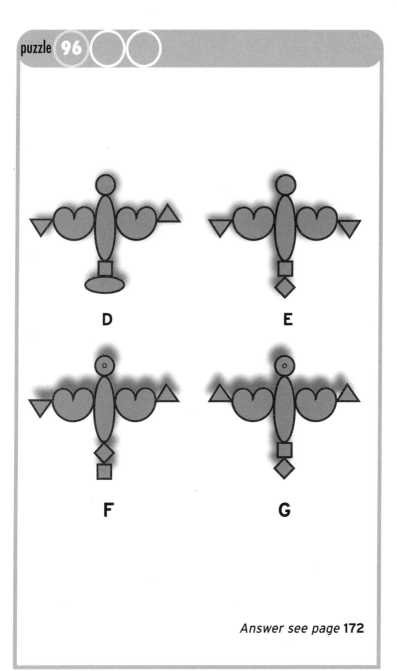

D

E

F

G

Answer see page **172**

Can you work out which diagram is the odd one out?

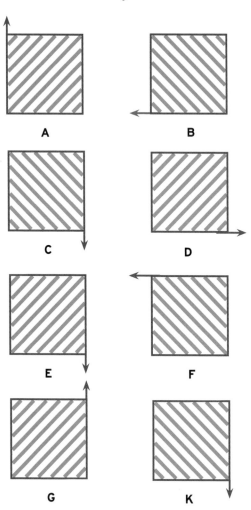

A

B

C

D

E

F

G

K

Answer see page **172**

These pieces, when fitted together correctly, make up a square. However, one piece is not needed. Can you work out which one it is?

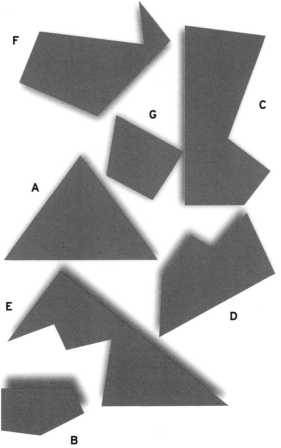

Answer see page 172

Can you work out what number would replace the question mark?

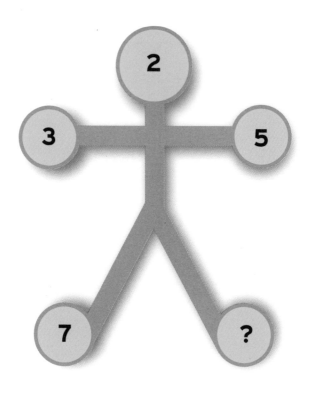

Answer see page 172

Can you find the odd number out?

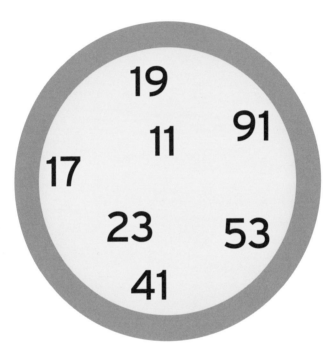

Answer see page **251**

This square follows a pattern. Can you unravel it and replace the question mark with a number?

Answer see page **172**

3	3	9	3
5	8	2	1
4	3	8	1
8	2	1	?

What is the correct time for Balloon E?

A 13 hours
18 min

B 28 hours
35 min

C 16 hours
21 min

D 7 hours
19 min

E a) 13 hours 29 min
b) 12 hours 35 min
c) 7 hours 12 min
d) 12 hours 7 min

Answer see page **172**

Can you work out which two models cannot be made from this layout?

Answer see page 172

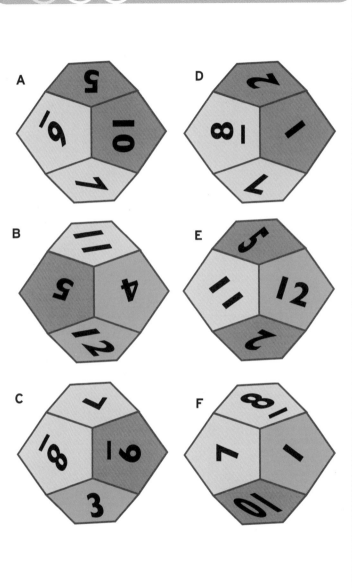

Can you spot the odd one out?

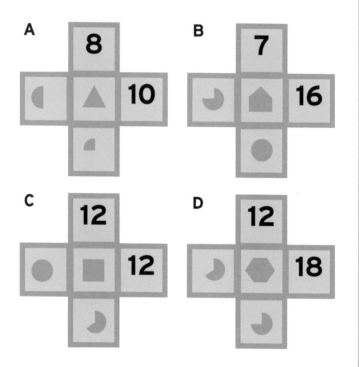

Answer see page 172

4	8	3	2	7	5	6	1	9	4	?
2	3	7	6	2	4	1	5	3	7	90
8	7	3	2	4	6	9	1	4	2	101
4	3	6	8	2	9	7	6	8	7	115
3	2	1	6	9	8	8	7	3	4	101
6	2	3	8	4	1	9	7	2	6	104
7	3	4	2	1	9	4	5	3	5	100
6	5	4	3	2	8	4	7	6	1	103
3	5	2	1	8	6	9	4	3	7	106
6	8	7	3	2	4	5	9	5	6	109

103 98 99 100 81 117 121 109 99 107

Find a number that could replace the question mark.
Each colour represents a number under 10.

Answer see page 173

Find a number that could replace the question mark.
Each colour represents a number under 10.

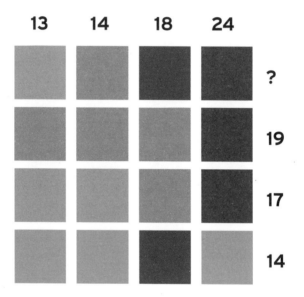

13	14	18	24	
				?
				19
				17
				14

Answer see page **173**

Find a number that could replace the question mark. Each colour represents a number under 10.

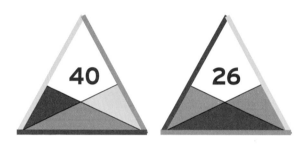

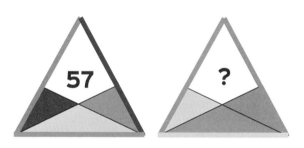

Answer see page **173**

These pieces, when fitted together correctly, form a square. However, one wrong piece is among them. Can you work out which one it is?

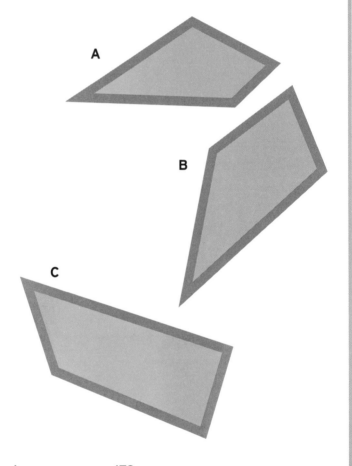

Answer see page 173

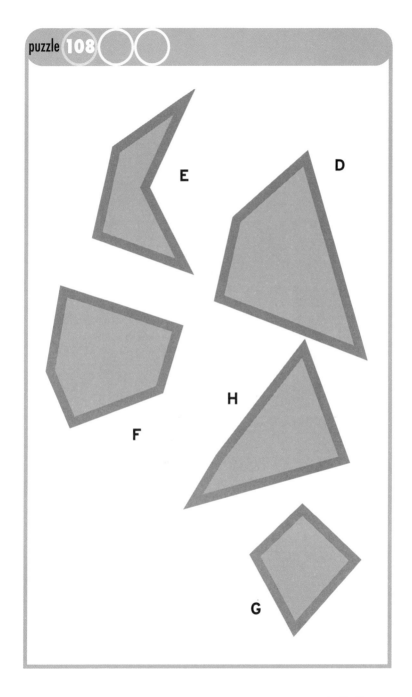

Find a number that could replace the question mark.
Each colour represents a number under 10.

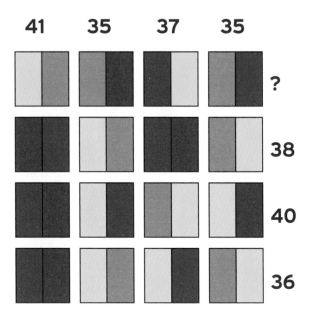

Answer see page **173**

If the black arrow pulls in the direction indicated, will the load rise or fall?

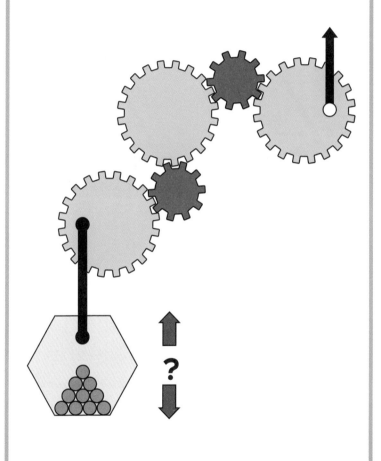

Answer see page **173**

Find a number that could replace the question mark.
Each colour represents a number under 10.

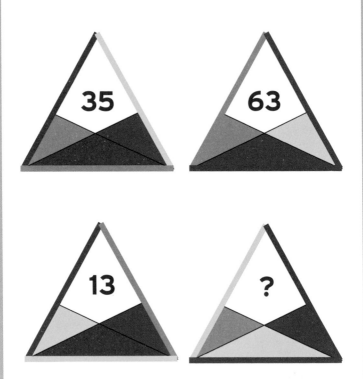

Answer see page 173

Take 9 matches or
toothpicks and lay
them out in 3 triangles.
By moving 3 matches
try to make 5 triangles.

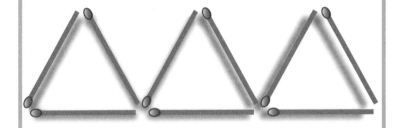

Answer see page **173**

Find a number that could replace the question mark.
Each colour represents a number under 10.

13	14	18	24	

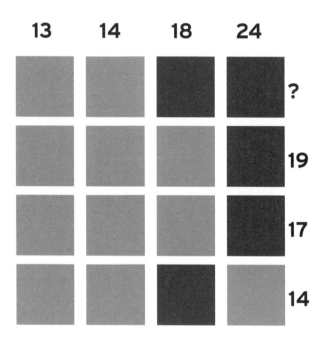

?

19

17

14

Answer see page 174

Find a number that could replace the question mark.
Each colour represents a number under 10.

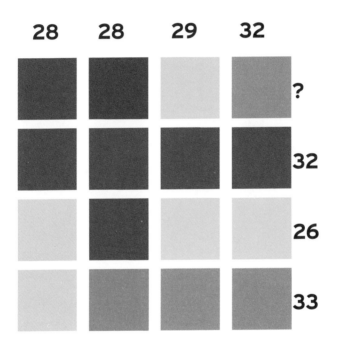

28	28	29	32

?

32

26

33

Answer see page **174**

Which of the shapes opposite comes next in this series?

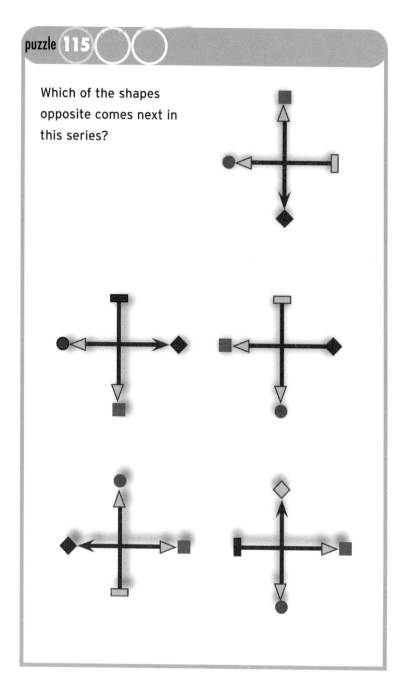

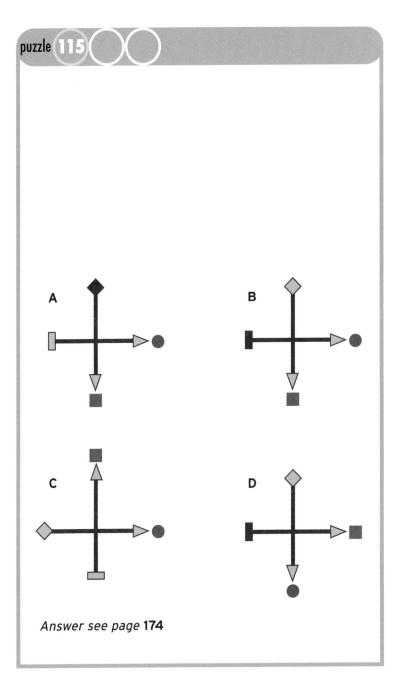

A

B

C

D

Answer see page 174

Have a look at the strange watches below. By cracking the logic that connects them you should be able to work out what time should be shown on the face of the fifth watch.

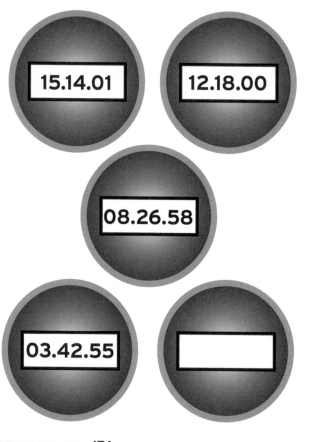

Answer see page **174**

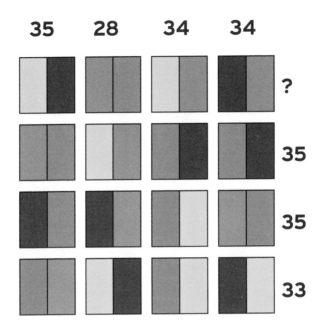

35   28   34   34

?
35
35
33

Find a number that could replace the question mark.
Each colour represents a number under 10.

Answer see page 174

Which of the following forms a perfect circle when combined with the diagram at the top?

Answer see page **174**

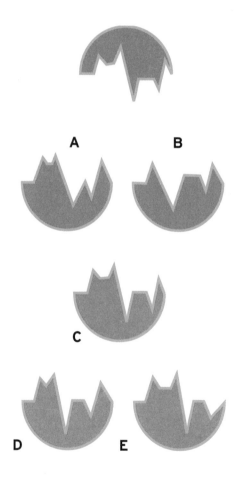

Which cube can be made using:

A

B

C

D

E

Answer see page **174**

Which of the shapes on the right can be constructed
using this layout?

Answer see page **174**

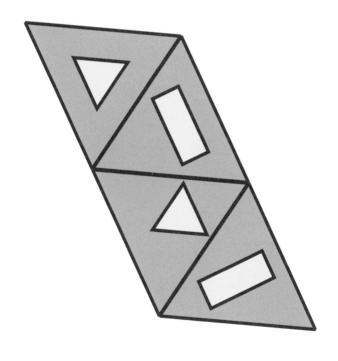

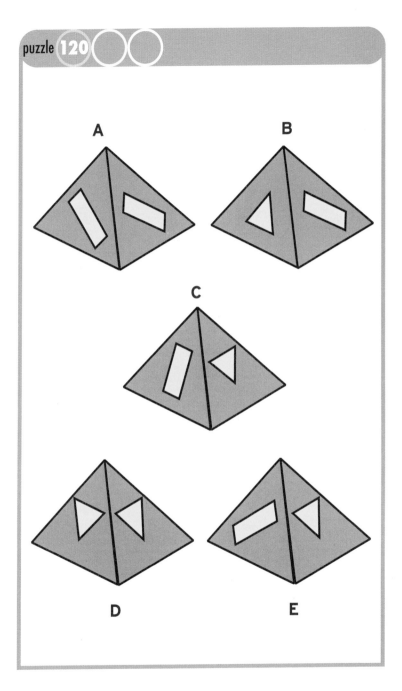

A

B

C

D

E

Which is the odd one out?

A

B

C

D

E

Answer see page **174**

What comes next in the sequence?

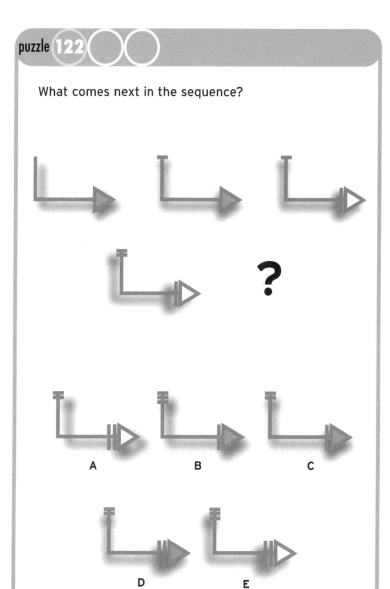

?

A

B

C

D

E

Answer see page 174

Try to work out the fiendish logic behind this series of clocks and replace the question mark.

Answer see page **175**

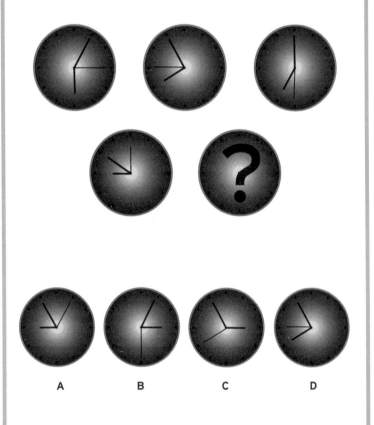

Which is the odd one out?

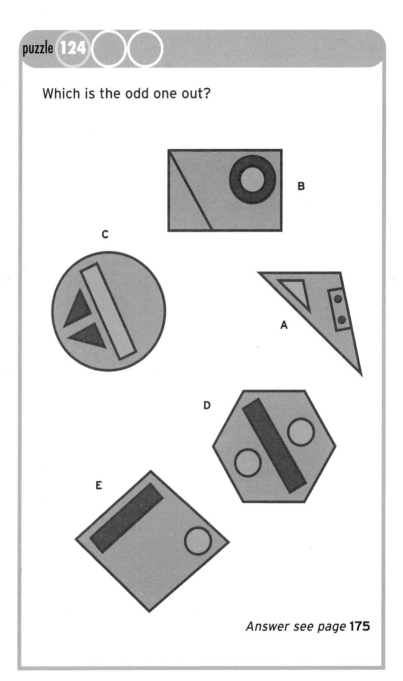

Answer see page **175**

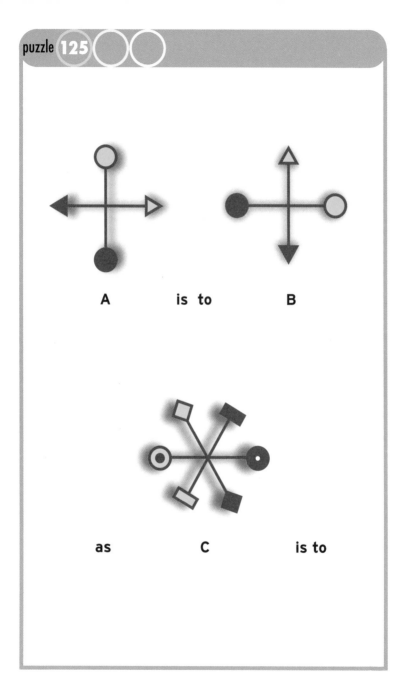

A   is to   B

as   C   is to

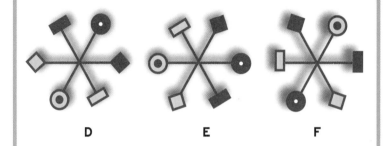

D   E   F

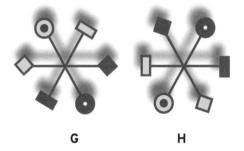

G   H

Answer see page 175

The values of the segments are 3 consecutive numbers under 10. The yellow is worth 7 and the sum of the segments equals 50. What do the blue and green segments equal?

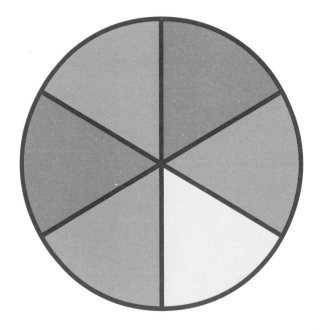

Answer see page **175**

How much is the question mark worth?

Answer see page **175**

Look at these triangles. What geometrical shape should logically be placed in the fourth triangle?

Answer see page **175**

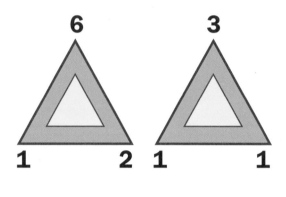

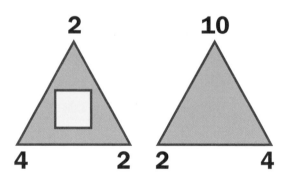

Where should another dot belong?

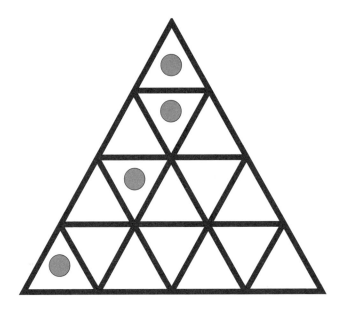

Answer see page **175**

Which comes next in the sequence?

A **B** **C**

D **E**

Answer see page 175

Which is the odd one out?

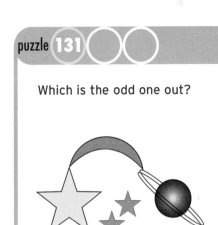

A

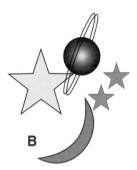

B

C

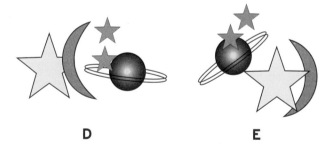

D **E**

Answer see page **175**

The pictures illustrate different views of one cube.
What does the hidden side indicated by the X look like?

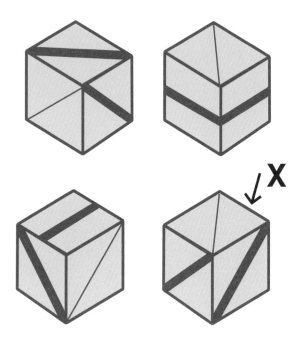

A   B   C

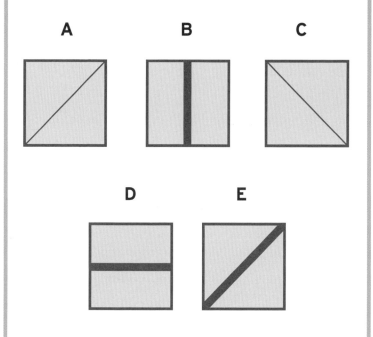

D   E

Answer see page 175

Answers

1 B and H.

2 16. All the other numbers can be divided by 3.

3 Top half: + +; bottom half: + -.

4 E. Turn the diagram by 90° clockwise.

5 A and L. The numbers are 3, 4, 6 and 9.

6 5 x 4 ÷ 2 + 7 = 17.

7 C. The number in the middle is the sum of the squares of the numbers at the points of the triangles. C does not fit this pattern.

8 2. It relates to the number of shapes that enclose each figure.

9 Indigo and Violet (colours of the rainbow).

10 D.

11 Top half: x ÷; bottom half: ÷ x.

12 B, F and N.

13 4 moons. Sun = 9; Moon = 5; Cloud = 3.

14 26. The digits in each of the other balls add up to 10.

15

16 8. Subtract the bottom left corner from the top left corner. Now subtract the bottom right corner from the top right corner, then subtract this answer from the first difference and put the number in the middle.

17 Three clouds and a moon. Sun = 6; Moon = 7; Cloud = 9.

18 The diamond. It is a closed shape.

19 3. The numbers in each wheel add up to 30.

20 6 + 7 + 11 ÷ 3 x 2 + 5 - 12 = 9.

21 27. A number in the first circle is squared and the product is put in the corresponding segment of the second circle. The original number is then cubed and that product is put in the corresponding segment of the third circle.

22 F. The numbers made up of odd numbers are reversed.

23 One arrow. Oval = 1, Arrow = 2, Diamond = 3.

24 C. In the others the small shapes added together result in the large shape.

25 6:50. The minute hand moves back 5, 10 and 15 minutes, while the hour hand moves forward 1, 2 and 3 hours.

26 35. Star = 6; Tick = 3; Cross = 17; Circle = 12.

27 C. In all other cases, the biggest shape is also the smallest.

28 C. The minute hand moves forward 5 minutes and the hour hand moves forward 3 hours.

29 C. The smallest segment is rotated 90 degrees clockwise. The middle segment remains static. The largest segment is rotated 90° anti-clockwise.

30 B.

31

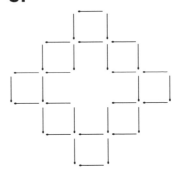

32 B. There is no triangle intersection on this one.

33 B. In all other cases the smaller circle is within the larger circle.

34 B. The minute hand moves back 15 minutes and the hour hand moves forward 3 hours.

35 H. The symbols are reflections of each oher.

36 B. The sequence here is minus one dot, plus two dots; the box rotates one place anti-clockwise for each dot added or subtracted.

37 E and M.

38 R. Multiply the value of the three earliest letters, based on their value in the alphabet, by 2. The answer goes in the opposite triangle. I (9) x 2 = 18 (R).

39 4 x 7 ÷ 2 + 8 + 9 x 6 ÷ 3 = 62.

40 42. Multiply the top right number by the bottom left number or the top left number by the bottom right number.

41 D is wrong because the dot is in 3 shapes. In all the others the dot is in 2 shapes.

42 11. The colours are worth Brown 1, Green 2, Orange 3, Yellow 4, Pink 5, Red 6, Purple 7. Add the outer numbers in each segment and place in the center of the next segment clockwise.

43 D.

44 3. The numbers rotate anti-clockwise from one square to the next and decrease by 2 each time.

45 9. Multiply the values in the same segments in wheels 2 and 3 and put the answer in the next segment in wheel 1, going clockwise.

46 Add the number of segments in column 1 to the number of segments in column 3. Draw this number of segments into column 2.

47 15. Take the number of minutes in the hours, add the minutes and divide by 10. Ignore the remainder.

48 E. Add two circles and two lines, take away one of each, repeat. The pattern is also rotated by 90° anti-clockwise each time.

49 27. Add all the numbers for each square. For Yellow add 5, for Green subtract 5. Then swap the numbers in adjacent Yellow and Green squares.

50 C.

51 A. Each ring contains one cross more than the previous example, and the first and last cross in each adjacent circle are level.

52 F. The circles and squares become squares and circles, respectively. The largest element loses all internal elements.

53 Starting at opposite ends the symbols move alternately 1 and 2 steps to the other end of the grid in a boustrophedon.

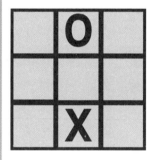

54 A.

55 D. Add consecutive clockwise corners of the first diamond and place the sum on the corresponding second corner. Add the four numbers of the first together and place the sum in the middle of the second.

56 No. 2. Take the first digit of the weight from the second to arrive at new number.

57 B. Each time the square becomes the circle, the triangle the square, and the circle the triangle.

58 92. Multiply the numbers on the diagonally opposite corners of each square and add the products. Put the sum in the third square along.

59 3:13. Start time A minus Finish A equals Finish B. Start time B minus Finish B equals Finish C, etc.

60 D. It is the only one to which a circle can be added where the triangle overlaps the circle and a right-angled line runs parallel to the whole of one side of the triangle.

61 C. Each row and column must contain two Orange and two Green squares.

62 B.

63 3.

64 J. All of the others have a matching partner.

65 E. All elements consist of 3 straight lines except 'E', which consists of 4 straight lines.

66 2.

67 44. The numbers increase clockwise first missing one spoke, then two at the fourth step. Each circle increases by a different amount (2, 3, 4).

68 B.

69 B. The others all have an equal number of straight lines and curves.

70 The corresponding sections in each wheel should contain a shaded section in each compartment.

71 Starting with a vertical line reflect the dot first against that line and then each following line in a clockwise direction.

72 F. The small and large elements become large and small, respectively.

73 9. The numbers rotate clockwise and increase by 1 each time.

74 B. It is the only one to have an odd number of horizontal lines.

75 C. The number of small circles equals the number of edges of the shape, except for C, where there is one more circle than there are edges.

76 10. Add 2 to each value, place sum in corresponding position in next triangle, then subtract 3, and add 2 again.

77 18. Multiply the numbers in the outer section, reverse the product and put it in the middle of the next section.

78 20. Multiply hours by minutes and divide by 3 to get the number of the rider.

79 Forward, back, forward, back.

80 48. In each box of four numbers, multiply the top two numbers, put the product in the bottom right box, then subtract the top right number from the bottom right one and put the difference in the bottom left box.

81

82 Yellow (the numbers are added to give the totals).

83 B. Each arch moves closer to its opposite end by an equal amount each time.

84 1956. The numbers represent the leap years clockwise around the triangles starting at the apex. Miss one leap year each time.

85 9:05. The minute hand goes forward 25 minutes, the hour hand back by 5 hours.

86 13.

87 B. It is the only figure that does not have three boxes in one row.

88 C.